IT'S A DOG'S LIFE, CHARLIE BROWN

Books by Charles M. Schulz

IT'S A DOG'S LIFE, CHARLIE BROWN

A NEW *PEANUTS®* BOOK

by Charles M. Schulz

HOLT, RINEHART AND WINSTON
New York · Chicago · San Francisco

SBN: 03–030835–6

Printed in the United States of America

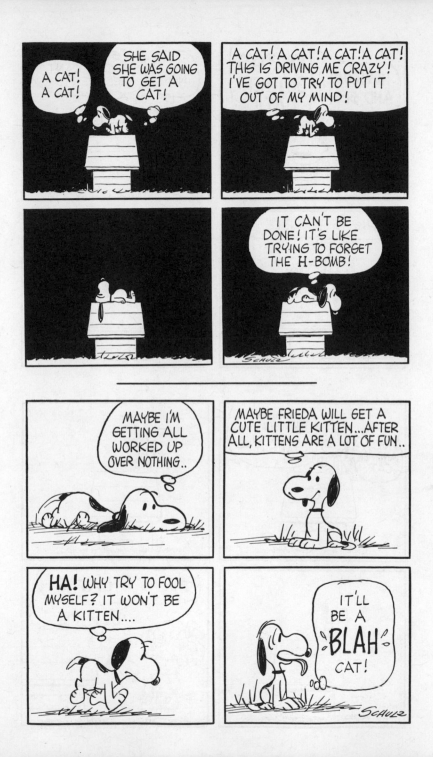